Finally Met Along the Way

[illegible]
Hope you enjoy
these short stories about
Vermonters...
[illegible]

Finally Met
Along the Way

A Third Collection of Short Stories
About People in Vermont

Cornelius "Con" Hogan

2010

MANUFACTURED IN THE UNITED STATES OF AMERICA

Library of Congress Control Number 2010939452
ISBN 978-0-915010-50-9

For ordering information
or to purchase additional copies, please contact

East Hill Farm
324 Gonyeau Road
Plainfield, VT 05667-9669
chogan@conhogan.com

Designed and published by
Sutter House
P.O. Box 212
Lititz, PA 17543

To

Bill and Kathie Moulton,

who made a lot of these stories possible

Contents

About the Author

Cornelius "Con" Hogan and his young family moved to Vermont in early 1972 from central New Jersey where he had spent seven years of work in corrections, beginning as a Correction Officer. He spent another seven years in that work in Vermont as Deputy Commissioner and later as Commissioner of Corrections.

He and his wife, Jeannette, and daughter, Ruth, along with Kathie and Bill Moulton, their farm partners, operate East Hill Farm Family Riding Center, which was established in 1976 in Plainfield, Vermont. The Hogans' son, Neil, and his family also live on East Hill Farm.

Over the years they became part of a remarkable neighborhood of self-sufficient people, many of whom had roots going back to a much earlier Vermont.

In his professional work, Hogan was fortunate to have worked in five different administrations of four different governors of both parties, ending his government career as Secretary of Human Services under Governors Richard Snelling and Howard Dean.

While he has slowed his pace somewhat, he is still a respected international consultant on children's well-being issues, working in far-flung places such as the U.K., the Netherlands, Australia, Chile, Ireland, Norway, and, most recently, Northern Ireland.

Throughout his life in Vermont, Con and his family have enjoyed and savored the independence and character of everyday Vermonters and their leaders.

Con is a co-author of *At the Crossroads: The Future of Health Care in Vermont* and *Gridlock: The Unhealthy Politics of Health Care in Vermont.* He is author of *Outcomes: A Framework for Improved Well-Being* along with several books about Vermont people—*Met Along the Way: Short Stories About People in Vermont,* and *Also Met Along the Way: More Short Stories About People in Vermont.* He is hoping that this book, *Finally Met Along the Way: A Third Collection of Short Stories About People in Vermont,* will be a worthy successor to the earlier two books.

Preface

I've written and published previously two "Met Along the Way" books, and I've come to enjoy the process of remembering and writing these stories. I continue to get positive comments about the first two books. So we'll now plunge into this third and last set of short stories about Vermont people.

In this third book, I have broken one of my self-imposed rules; namely, only to write about people in Vermont. However, one of the recurring themes of the first two books, and this one, is that a number of stories are connected to the fascinating and sometimes strange world of prisons and corrections. The first story in this book, "The Element of Surprise," violates the Vermont-only rule. I hope the reader will forgive this transgression.

As in previous books, stories fall in general chronological order, which can result in an imbalance of characters and stories. Someday I'll integrate and organize all of the stories in a more useful way for the reader.

This will probably be my last "Met Along the Way." The process of remembering and thinking out loud about all the wonderful people I've met on the journey has been very gratifying to me and hopefully amusing to the reader.

ACKNOWLEDGMENTS

My first and deepest thank you goes to Douglass Livingston, my publisher from Sutter House, whose patience with me reflected our long-term, 46-year friendship.

I am equally thankful to Tim Newcomb, who provided the dead-on cartoons and covers for these books. His brand went a long way to making the books as successful as they have been.

Again I received the never-ending support of my wife, Jeannette, who carefully reviewed the manuscript and made timely suggestions to improve it. It is difficult to step out of one's own skin to criticize oneself.

The Element of Surprise

This story, as I mentioned in the Foreword, violates one of the rules that I adopted when I started writing this series, in that this story is about a man and situation that occurred well before my family and I moved to Vermont. But because it is a story about life in corrections work, and since I've spent so many years connected to that work in Vermont, I decided to break the rule.

I began my work in corrections field in 1964 as a prison guard. The term "corrections officer" was just coming into vogue. In many ways, those years preceded the professionalism currently seen in the work of today.

An example of how things were done was in the training of officers. There was no formal training. A new officer was simply assigned to an experienced officer for a week and then to a second officer for a second week, and then a third officer for a third week. At the end of that time, it was "sink or swim" time. The new officer was expected to have learned enough to survive in that tough world.

My first assignment as a new officer was with Officer John Hoadley. Hoadley had responsibility for a living unit of about 100 young men from the ages of 17 to 23. I was to observe Hoadley carefully to understand what worked and what did not work and then to apply those lessons when I ended up having responsibility for one of the living units.

Things under Hoadley's watch were okay, but occasionally it was a touch nerve-wracking on his unit. Things were just noisy enough to make you wonder if the noise might be hiding something. You never knew what the something was, but the assumption was that it would not be a good something. But Hoadley always got to the 9 P.M. lockdown time with a smile on his face and a joke for a couple of the inmates who had cleanup responsibilities just after lockdown. There was always a little too much trash on the floors, and a spilled soda or two, but all in all, things seemed to be in pretty good shape at the end of Hoadley's shift.

My second week was with Officer Barnhardt. On this shift, things were very different. There was just too much noise, of tin cans being used as bongo drums, high levels of cigarette smoke (cigarettes were legal but were supposed to be controlled), and the constant searching and counting of inmates to make sure they were all there. You always had the feeling that, just around the next corner, something bad might be going on. It was frankly a nerve-wracking shift, which was repeated every night of the training week. I recall going home completely exhausted at the end of one of those shifts. I was definitely not going to model my work and supervision after Barnhardt's approach.

The third week I was assigned to John Mongeon. Mongeon was not a big man, as prison guards go, and he wasn't constantly giving orders as both Hoadley and Barnhardt did. He seemed to quietly amble around the living unit while the inmates kept the unit in good shape. Inmates would voluntarily be cleaning the floors, cigarettes were extinguished in clean coffee cans with sand, music was very soft in the background, and at the 9 P.M. lockdown the prisoners would voluntarily make their way to their cells without being told to do so. In the case of both Hoadley and Barnhardt, lockdown instructions to the prisoners had been repeated over and over. Mongeon never said a word ... but good things just happened ... all of the time.

After the shift was over, and the inmates were safely locked in their cells, I approached Mongeon in his small office. I just had to know what his secret was. I couldn't figure it out just by observing. I needed an explanation.

I asked Officer Mongeon why he seemed to be so successful in maintaining such apparently constructive control without having to bark constant orders and directives to the people in his charge. "You really want to know?" asked Mongeon. "Yes," I said.

At that point Mongeon turned his back on me, the way comedians do when they are putting on a "face" for their next routine. He turned around to face me. He had taken out his false front teeth and worked up a foam in his mouth. He then reached into his back pocket and pulled out a little rubber hammer and simply said, with spittle flying from his mouth, "They never know what I'm going to do next." I had learned something fundamental that I would never find in any book. I'm not saying I ever used that particular technique, but I knew I could if I ever needed to.

The Drummer

Music has always been a part of my life and my family's life. I can trace that interest and proficiency back to the 1920s and 1930s, when my mother played piano for the silent movies (but that's another story).

My expression of music primarily came as a member of a variety of pop, folk, and bluegrass bands during my adolescent and college years. It has culminated in 30 years of playing bluegrass with the same group, Cold Country Bluegrass. It includes our farm partner Bill Moulton, a terrific mandolin player, whose dad was a guitarist for the famed Pony Boys of Vermont in the 1940s and 1950s. The band also includes Craig Whipple, a director of the Vermont Department of Forest and Parks and a friendly competitor in the horse business, and my wife, Jeannette, who plays the string bass. We're also fortunate to have the amazing and well-known Tony Washburn, fiddler and mentor extraordinaire, play regularly with us.

However, this story precedes our bluegrass period. Bill Moulton decided we should form a country and western band. This was in the period when Johnny Cash, Waylon Jennings, and Willie Nelson were in their peak and high creative years, and our band was playing a lot of their songs.

At one point in this short-lived quest, we found ourselves playing at Mac's Place, a "bring your own" dance hall establishment in Sutton, in the most northern reaches of Vermont. At that time we were a four-piece band, with Bill playing lead guitar, me on backup guitar, Art Edelstein playing electric bass (currently a music critique and music feature writer for the *Times Argus*), and drummer Jay Majowski, a forester friend of Bill's, who was playing with us for the first time that evening.

Things started off well. It was a large, well-oiled crowd that was into the music and dancing. As the night developed though, we noticed that in each song we played, the drum beat behind us grew just a little faster. It turns out Majowski was drinking as much as the crowd was that

evening. But he was behind us, and we didn't get a sense of "how much." The more he drank, the faster his drumming became. And the faster we played as a result of the steadily quickening beat, the more and faster the crowd danced. It was a wild scene, until ...

Suddenly, as we were in the middle of much-too-fast "Folsom Prison Blues," there was a huge crash behind us, and everything came to an immediate halt. The crowd was looking intently at the stage, and when we turned around to see what had happened, there was Majowski in a heap next to the drum set, which had also collapsed in a pile.

The place went crazy as a large cheer went up from crowd, encouraging Jay to regain his feet. But he couldn't. He was nearly completely incapacitated.

I think that this was a signal that our days as a country band were numbered. It was also a lesson to the effect that band members should not drink and drum.

Alfred Chase—A Remarkable Man

Alfred "Crazy" Chase was born in Morrisville at the turn of the 20th century. Much of the information in this story about his remarkable life comes from Tony Washburn, an accomplished musician, who has lived in central Vermont most of his adult life.

Another source was Ethel Ryan, born in 1918, who grew up in Middlesex and remembered Mr. Chase well. She now resides at the Heaton Woods in Montpelier. Ethel particularly remembers her times with her parents, who every Saturday evening would take Ethel to the square and the round dancing in Middlesex for which Mr. Chase and his band would play. Ethel also remembers many of the musicians who would play with Alfred's band at different times, including Helen Bouska, on piano, and Walter Brooks, on drums.

Tony came to know Mr. Chase about 1947, in the many dance hall settings of the era. One favorite was the regular Friday night dance at the Wolcott Town Hall. Mr. Chase, in those days had the "Chase Orchestra," which consisted of drums, piano, bass, saxophone, guitar, and Mr. Chase himself on fiddle. Some of the renowned players of the time in central Vermont regularly played with the orchestra, including Mrs. Shackett who had a collection of sheet music of the popular songs of the day. One of the stalwarts of the group was Al Roberge, a fine saxophone player and a dance caller. Many of the stories that Tony Washburn has today about Crazy Chase were passed along by Al.

Chase often performed in women's clothes. This garb included what today we would call "old-lady clothes," including a hair net, and high-heel shoes. Overall, Vermonters at the time might have been put off by this display, but they were accepting and tolerant, probably because of his amazing skills on the fiddle. He was also a naturally happy and intelligent man. He was a magnet for the young people, who were totally fascinated by the sounds and noises that Chase could make with his fiddle. Between sets at the dance halls, Chase would entertain the kids with, for example, barnyard sounds that would flow from the fiddle. Chicks, cows, dogs, pigs—all were fair game for making the fiddle "talk." It is said that one of his favorite sounds was to make the fiddle "fart" as though it was a horse. One can only imagine these zany moments.

In today's world, Mr. Chase might have been labeled an idiot savant as a result of his fiddle skills. It is said that he could imitate any and all songs instantaneously when hearing a song for the first time. To the untrained ear it sounded like he was well practiced on a given song, when in reality he was hearing it for the first time, and was only a microsecond behind the beat as he immediately mimicked what he was hearing.

He could also take the horsehair off one end of his fiddle bow, insert the bow underneath the strings, reattach the horsehair, and play full chords on the fiddle, something that is simply unheard of. His verbal comment at the end of one of these chordal masterpieces would be something like, "That sure sounds pretty, don't it?"

He could make a fiddle sound like you were in a dream, with unmatched clarity and melodic skill.

At one point, a local businessman in Morrisville decided to take Chase to Boston, to the New England Conservatory of Music to test his remarkable capacity. They visited a professor of music who was a renowned violinist in his own right. The story goes that the professor played a Paganini solo on the violin, which was a complex and fast piece of work, and played steadily for about five minutes. After he was finished playing the piece, Chase picked up his own old fiddle and replayed the Paganini piece note for note, dynamic for dynamic, perfectly. It must have been an astounding moment.

This ability came naturally to Crazy Chase. He had no conception that his skills were not normal.

Tony Washburn was about 15 years old when he first played guitar and sang with Mr. Chase and Mrs. Shackett's band. But it wasn't long before Chase's fiddle playing had transfixed Tony Washburn.

Chase didn't drive and had to depend on others to get around, usually a member of his band at the time. He eked out a living tuning pianos, which was an easy chore for him as he had what is known as perfect pitch. In other words, he could recognize or produce a perfect G—and all he had to do was think about it, and not even hear it. There are very few people

with this capacity. His pitch was so attuned that he could be a passenger in a car and hear the hum of the tires on the road, and then tell the driver that they were driving in the key of D. He further honed this particular skill to the point that he could associate the pitch of tires with the speed of the car, so that at any moment he could tell the driver how fast he was going based on the hum of the pitch that the tires were making.

Chase also had some remarkable smoking habits. There are stories that when he asked for a cigarette someone would give him an entire pack. He would then take all of them out of the pack and light them all at the same time. He wasn't showing off in the classical sense; that's just how he smoked.

Another favorite technique was to take a one and five-eights tin of tobacco, punch a hole in the side of the tin, insert a pipe stem, and smoke the entire tin.

At one point the people who ran the dance halls had to stop him from smoking inside the building because, if given a cigar, he could fill up the entire building with smoke due to the intensity with which he smoked the cigar in a matter of moments.

Crazy Chase died in 1960 after having lived his entire life in greater central Vermont—at various times in Morrisville, Wolcott, Worcester, Duxbury, Waterbury, and Middlesex.

Once in a while someone passes through that is so special, we forgive the strangeness of the quirks that come with them. Alfred Chase was a fellow, so obviously talented beyond anything that anyone here had ever seen, that he was viewed with a sense of awe more than amusement.

Quiet Advice

People in government, in order to appear thorough and impartial, often enter into complex and comprehensive processes that sometimes can be more trouble than they are worth.

I fell into that trap in the mid 1970s when I was Commissioner of Corrections. The Governor was Richard Snelling. One of the State's agendas at the time was to replace the county jails. Most had been built in the mid 1800s. In the late 1960s, the State of Vermont had taken them over from the counties after a series of scandals. They were now being asked to serve well beyond their capacities. With the closing of the old Windsor Prison in 1974, inmates had been sent to county jails in Woodstock, Rutland, Burlington, and St. Johnsbury, and these jails were now very overcrowded.

Corrections Commissioner Kent Stoneman made me the public point man on the project. My job was to find sites to replace these old, outmoded, and even inhumane facilities. As a good bureaucrat I enlisted the Buildings Division and its longtime leader, Irving Bates, to spearhead the search for sites, with the theory being that the more sites we had to choose from the easier it would be to find places to consider for the replacement facilities.

It wasn't long before Irv Bates and I had the entire state in an uproar. No community wanted a new jail facility in its town, nor did the public even want to keep the old facilities. Selectboard after selectboard went on record to oppose the State's push to put a correctional facility into their backyard. The resistance reached the point where it was becoming a visible and somewhat noisy political issue for Governor Snelling, whose sensitivity to local concerns was well developed and attuned.

One morning my secretary, Fern Barnes, told me that the Governor's office had called earlier and that I was requested to pay the Governor a quick visit. I dutifully made my way to the fifth floor and was immediately escorted into Governor Snelling's office.

In a very few words, the Governor told me that I was really stirring up the political pot, and that the local politics of the situation was beginning to affect other local agendas that the Governor had on his plate. He summed up his position to me in one sentence.

"Con," he said, "all you have to do is tell me the best site for the first replacement correctional facility, and be prepared to rationally defend your pick. I will then announce that we have chosen the new site, and all of the towns that were not picked will stand up and cheer."

It was quiet, thoughtful, incisive, and effective advice. And more importantly, it worked.

Harold Muzzy, Dowser Extraordinaire

In my first book of short stories, *Met Along the Way*, I told a story about my efforts to learn to dowse during the early years of our life in Vermont. What I did not say in that story was what the circumstances were of my first exposure to dowsing.

When our family moved to Vermont in 1972, we moved into an old rambling farmhouse on Muzzy Road in Berlin. The road was named Muzzy Road because Harold Muzzy and his family lived on the road. Harold was also the longtime town road commissioner, who was wise in the ways of life in rural Vermont.

A quick aside from the flow of this impending story: Early in our relationship as good neighbors on the road, and after learning that Harold was the road commissioner, I asked Harold one day how he knew when to wake up to go and plow the roads. His quick answer was that he slept with his arm out the window. I tell you this because it gives the reader quick insight about Harold and his way of thinking. But back to the story.

Soon after we moved into the old house, we realized that we were having some septic issues. There was constant gurgling coming from the sinks and toilets. We knew we had to do some repair work. But where was the septic tank? We couldn't find any sign of a tank outside and around the house, and we had no idea who might have put the tank in many years ago. So we approached Harold to gain a little of his local knowledge, as he had lived on the road for many years.

Harold said of course he could help, and I asked how. He said he would simply dowse for the tank and locate it for us.

This was my first exposure to even the idea of dowsing. I had never heard of dowsing before. I quickly learned that a person skilled in the art of dowsing could take a forked branch, preferably off of an apple or willow tree, hold it tightly in his hands, and then move slowly across the ground until some force of nature would try and pull the branch from the hands, which was the signal that there was water at that point beneath the ground, and that the water was pretty close to the surface.

It sounded like fun to Jan and me, so one bright Saturday fall morning, Harold showed up at the house with his dowsing stick, and we skeptics were to get our first lesson in the art of dowsing.

Harold seriously began the task at hand. He tightly gripped the apple branch and systematically began to slowly move back and forth across the lawn. There was dead silence as Harold began to concentrate heavily on the strength of the resistance in his hands. In about 10 minutes the point of the stick began to almost violently pull directly toward the ground, pulling Harold's hands and arms toward the ground. We were all quite speechless. Harold, with firm seriousness then declared, "The septic system is right here and is about two feet deep into the ground."

We immediately dug a test hole and, sure enough, quickly came upon the concrete lid to the tank.

Later, we arranged to have the tank cleaned out, which cured the problems that we had.

It was about two years later when another neighbor told us that Harold and his family had once lived in the house that we were now living in, and that Harold had, in fact, installed the septic tank and system.

The Department of Pubic Safety

Rapidly changing technology can sometimes get ahead of our ability to use it well and occasionally get us into trouble. A story in the late 1970s comes to mind.

The Vermont Department of Public Safety had an assignment from the Vermont Legislature to produce an important report about something or other. This was in the early days of spell-checking on computer-generated documents.

We have all become victims of spell-checking that approves the spelling of a particular word but clearly is not the proper word for the meaning being transmitted.

This happened to the Department of Public Safety. The Department dutifully wrote the report after several months of research. Early one morning, their communications officer came to the State House and distributed the weighty report onto each and every chair of the representatives and senators.

The only problem was that in the boldest and brightest font available, on the front page of the report, was the title of the report, followed by the organization that had written and distributed the report, The Department of Pubic Safety.

The reader can judge the reaction to the report.

Martha's Vineyard and the Vermont Legislative Resolution

Most of the time, the affairs and issues of individual states remain within those states. But there are times when states work together for their common interest. Interstate parole compacts and interstate waste districts are but two examples of that common work.

In 1974 there was an interesting possibility that never happened. The circumstances were related to problems that Martha's Vineyard was having with taxation policies of the Commonwealth of Massachusetts. In the minds of the Vineyarders, the regulations discriminated against those living on the Island.

It was a long-simmering feud between the Islanders and the state bureaucracy that was increasingly spilling over into the *Boston Globe* in particular. At one point in the feud, the Island threatened to secede from the Commonwealth of Massachusetts.

This did not go unnoticed by the sharp-eyed and always opportunistic members of the Vermont Legislature at the time. Immediately, creative minds sprang into action.

I cannot remember the actual text of the Resolution that was passed by the Vermont Legislature at that time, but the sense of it went something like this:

> **Whereas,** the great Commonwealth of Massachusetts has failed in its duty of fair and equitable taxation of citizens of Martha's Vineyard, and
>
> **Whereas,** the Islanders of Martha's Vineyard have expressed an interest and desire to secede from the Commonwealth of Massachusetts, and
>
> **Whereas,** the Green Mountain State of Vermont, which has been blessed with great natural beauty and strong and independent people, and

Whereas, one of the economic realities that Vermont must deal with is the absence of a seaport,

Therefore, be it resolved that the State of Vermont offers to the Island of Martha's Vineyard, the opportunity to become part of the State of Vermont after it secedes from Massachusetts.

The resolution made the front page of the *Boston Globe,* and, in short order, the Islanders of Martha's Vineyard, with resolution in hand, were able to come to a new accommodation regarding taxes with the Commonwealth of Massachusetts.

Having been raised along the ocean in New Jersey and having loved the seashore over the course of my life, I couldn't help but muse about the possibilities of ... what if ...

Is It Uphill or Downhill of the Road?

We had been running our nacent horse business for about a year by 1977. Jeannette and I lived in Berlin on Muzzy Road, which was a long way from where we had purchased some land in South Plainfield. Our soon-to-be business partner, Kathie Gayer, was living in an old school bus on her property, which abutted ours, and we kept our tack for the three horses we owned, Cadence, Briar Rose, and Cory, in the basement of Gene Foss' home, which was located on the same road. Gene was the business manager for the Department of Corrections, Kathie was the personnel officer, and I was the Deputy Commissioner of Corrections at the time.

It soon became clear that we had to build a stable along with an indoor arena if we were serious about getting into the horse business.

At that time, there were fewer than ten indoor arenas in the entire State of Vermont, and we began the process of visiting every one of them to get the best ideas we could about building such a structure.

Over several months we gathered ideas and slowly began to plan the facility. We decided on the construction company Northern Design, which was founded by Andy Rudin, who gave us some estimates to put up the formidable structure. It was no small building, with the indoor arena part being 60 feet by 120 feet, plus another attached stable of 30 by 120. Now the process led us to the point of getting the permissions we needed to proceed.

I went to the Plainfield Town Hall and spoke with the town clerk. She advised me that the key person that I needed to talk with was Mr. Alan Farnham, the long-standing road commissioner for the town.

One spring day I was walking along Gonyeau Road, where we were planning to build both the stable and arena and our own home at a later date. Mr. Farnham was standing outside his pickup truck, admiring the remarkable view to the south. The elevation of the property on the southern side of Plainfield is about 1,600 feet.

I approached Mr. Farnham. All I had was a crude pencil drawing of what we thought the building and the land layout might look like, and I asked him if he could give me permission to build the facility.

Alan looked at the piece of paper straight on, then sideways to the left, then sideways to the right, and finally upside down. After a very long period of silence, he finally asked, "Will the barn be on the uphill side of this road or downhill of the road?" I quickly responded, "Why, Mr. Farnham, it will be on the downhill side of the road."

Alan Farnham smiled and simply said, "That's good ... it won't bother my road."

And that is how we got permission to build the facility, which is now, as this is being written, in its 34th year of providing horse services to many. Imagine what the process and expense would be to get that far today.

Alan Farnham since retired as Plainfield road commissioner and started his own contracting business. He has been an integral part of the success of the farm over the years as he has taken on one major project after another for us. I've occasionally reminded Alan that the barn is on the "downhill side of the road." I've often wondered if with today's rules and regulations that we could have succeeded in starting our 34-year-old operation today.

Seeing the U.S.A.

It was 1974 and the Governor and the Legislature had made the policy decision to close the old Weeks School for juveniles. In its heyday the Weeks School was the model of education and supervision for children who had either been designated as delinquent or in need of supervision by a Vermont District Court. But in the early 1970s, the old place had fallen into serious disrepair and the nature of the children served there was changing, as new ways of doing business resulted in fewer and fewer young people going to the school in the first place. New and alternative ways of keeping children with their families and communities were emerging. Those who remained at the school were thereby of a harder-to-handle nature and, as a result, were staying longer. The culture was quickly changing from a positive institutional culture to a negative and occasionally dangerous one.

Once the decision was made by Governor Snelling to close the school and replace it with a Job Corps, plans had to be made quickly for new and different placements for the young people who were leaving the school before it was scheduled to close. New group homes were started, and new community treatment programs were established. Special education in Vermont schools was maturing as the schools learned well how to handle children who, in the old days, had been quickly sent to the Weeks School.

Slowly and steadily the census at the school declined. The State was on a schedule that could not be delayed because of the expense of funding the new alternatives, plus the high cost of keeping the old school going, plus the fact that the facility already had been leased to an incoming federal Job Corps. This lease was one of the keys to being able to close the old facility.

For most of the young people, good, solid placements were being found. However, as the numbers remaining at the school became ever lower, to fewer than a dozen, the placements became harder to find. Kent

Stoneman, Commissioner of what was known as Department of SRS, and I, as Commissioner of Corrections, were responsible for the transition. As the deadline began to loom, we began to look nervously for some short-term alternatives for six young people that would buy some time that would allow the school to close on schedule.

Enter Rod and Diane Mott, two seasoned cottage parents who had been stalwarts at the Weeks School for many years. They knew the school, they knew the kids, and they understood the risks of not being able to close the school on time.

They came up with a marvelous idea. Why not take the six most difficult children to place, rent a Winnebago, and go off to see the country for a couple of months. It was a brilliant idea. It bought us time to work out these difficult placements, assured that the school would be closing on time, and it would be a great experience for these kids under the supervision and tutelage of two of the best "parents" we had at the school. We also agreed that, between the two departments, we had the authority to pull this off, without obtaining hard-to-get permissions and "okays"from those higher up. It would have been hard to explain to the State's budget director, or legislative leaders, for example, that we were renting a big Winnebago to give six tough kids a free tour of the U.S. countryside for a few months.

Rod and Diane were excited about the trip, and the big camper was rented and the kids were off.

For about a month things went well. Rod and Diane would call in faithfully every morning with a brief report as to where they were, what they had seen, and their plans for the coming day. On the home front, things were also going well. The placements for the remainder of the few left at the Weeks School were falling into place, and things were on schedule ... until ...

I happened to be in the office a little earlier than usual one day and took the early morning call from Diane myself. The conversation went something like this:

Me: Diane, good to hear from you. Where are you?

Diane: We came into New Orleans yesterday afternoon.

Me: How's the camper performing?

Diane: It's running beautifully, couldn't be better.
Me: How are your charges doing?
Diane: They have been doing fine ... until last night.
Me: What happened last night?
Diane: They all took off.
Me: Took off? What do you mean?
Diane: They left Rod and me and we don't know where they are.

You could have knocked me over with a feather. The enormity of the folly we had undertaken suddenly became crystal clear. Here were six tough kids, theoretically under the State of Vermont's supervision, running loose in New Orleans, a place that is made to order for getting into some significant trouble.

Stoneman and I conferred, along with the Motts. We decided to give the kids 12 hours to return before we blew the whistle, although knowing fully that the odds of all of them voluntarily returning were slim to none. But wait we did, at the same time anticipating the public and official criticism of what we had done.

Amazingly, at about 6 P.M., we got a call from Rod Mott. They had all returned ... intact. They were excited about what they had seen and were full of great stories for Rod and Diane of their short adventure.

We had dodged a big bullet. But there was another lesson embedded in all this. And that lesson was the power of positive human relationships. Rod and Diane had the reputation of being trusted cottage parents. They were known as being fair and even-handed in their dealings with the kids at the Weeks School. One can only imagine the personal bonds that were developed and enhanced by their many weeks on the road with these boys, seeing and experiencing things that they never could have expected to have experienced. Those bonds stood well during that day when the boys took off . . . and then returned.

I would love to know what happened to each of those young men. I have to believe that their time with Rod and Diane stood them well over these many years.

Daisy Mae

After Dick Snelling was elected to the office of Governor in 1990, I was privileged along with Tom Moore, his campaign manager, to be the first folks on the transition team. You can imagine the intensity of that period. The situation was super complicated due to the looming financial deficit.

I was working from 7 A.M. to 11 P.M. every day. Soon thereafter, the Governor was filling out his team with terrific people like Doug Wasik, Dick Chapman, Wibs McLain, and Jan Eastman.

During the week between Christmas and the New Year of 1991, we were having an 8 A.M. staff meeting with the Governor-elect. There were six or seven of us on board by that time. Jeanne Johnson, the Governor's personal and long-standing secretary, came quietly into the room with a note for me. Governor Snelling did not like interruptions so Jeanne was very discreet in giving me the note. The note told me that my wife, Jeannette, was in the outer room of the Governor's State House office and needed to see me for a moment, and that she had some fresh clothes for me (which I badly needed).

I considered the wisdom of simply getting up and leaving the meeting for a moment but thought better of it. Finally, in a moment of temporary bravery, I interrupted the meeting and said to the Governor, "I have to leave for a moment. My wife would like to see me. However, would you mind taking a one-minute break and come explain to her why I'm spending more time with you than I am with her."

To my relief, he immediately took the bait, and off we both went to the anteroom just off the State House ceremony room, which serves as the Governor-elect's State House office until he is officially installed as Governor. Jeannette was standing in the doorway with a bag full of clean clothes. The Governor, with his eyes flashing and best gubernatorial smile, took her hand to tell her what a great service I was doing for the State and much more.

Unbeknownst to me, Jan had just been to the dentist and had had one of her upper front teeth removed for some repair. She was standing there with pursed lips as the Governor continued on his charm offensive. Suddenly, she couldn't resist any longer and came forth with a broad smile from ear to ear … which immediately exposed her Daisy May tooth situation.

Dick Snelling never let on. He was amazingly gracious, and Jeannette positively wilted under the effusive compliments.

Our little greeting ended and the Governor and I went back to the staff meeting, never missing a beat.

Jeannette never got over that. We still laugh about it today. It was vintage Dick Snelling, who when moved could move mountains with his charm and intensity.

Roger's Comeback

Roger Kayhart was a well-known long-term farmer in Addison County. He was so well liked he was repeatedly elected and re-elected to the Vermont Legislature in the late 1980s to the mid 1990s. In the early 1990s he suffered a serious stroke. This was especially difficult for him as he had always been the life of the party and a very gregarious and friendly man. He was a big brawny man with a physique borne of his many years of hard labor on the Kayhart dairy farm.

One of Roger's endearing quirks was that at any party, in any place, one could count on him at some point to launch into the old song "You Are My Sunshine," a song written and performed by the Governor of Louisiana, Governor Jimmie Davis, around the turn of the 20th century. Everyone knew that song, and it wasn't long before everyone in the room would be roaring along singing at the top of their lungs ... all led by the boisterous Roger Kayhart.

It was 1993 when Roger suffered the serious stroke. It just about paralyzed him and left him voiceless, with only the ability to make the crudest of sounds in his effort to communicate. For Roger it must have been an excruciating time.

For more than 35 years my wife, Jeannette, and I have been participants of the Cold Country Bluegrass Band, which I described in an earlier story.

We've had the privilege of playing many great venues over many years, including a tour of the Ring of Kerry in Ireland, but one of our favorite venues was playing on Farmers' Night at the State House. For non Vermonters who will read this little book, Farmers' Night is a long-standing set of performances on Wednesday evenings in the well of the House of Representatives. Its history was began in the days when most of the legislators were farmers, as the winter months were their down time, which made it possible for them to serve as legislators. Also, travel from the far-flung corners of Vermont was much more difficult in those days than it is today, so Farmers' Night served the purpose of breaking up the long week for the many legislators who stayed in Montpelier during the session.

There have been some extraordinary acts and performances on those winter evenings, including the circus of the famous legislator Reid Lefevre, who brought his animals to perform in the well of the House. That must have been quite a sight. In my research for this story, I found an April 1947 copy of a *Life* magazine story on the circus. It had photos of ponies in the State House ceremonial room. Even today, Farmers' Night hosts performances from the Vermont Symphony Orchestra, noted Vermont poets, and other luminaries from the theater and the wide world of music.

Our Cold Country Bluegrass Band had the privilege of playing Farmers' Night for a number of years in the 1990s during the period when I was the Secretary of Human Services. I recall getting a note from a well-known legislator of that time, who, after hearing our band play, penned the following to me: "I'm glad you have an avocation beyond your work as Secretary of Human Services. You are going to need it."

But back to my story about Roger Kayhart.

The night that the band was to play in the House well, there was a buzz in the air. The word was that Roger was coming back to the State House that evening to make an appearance. The well of the House was packed full as we began our performance of old-time string music. One of the quirks that evening was that our guitarist, Craig Whipple, had a conflict and couldn't play with us that night. Will Lindner, the well-known writer and musician with Banjo Dan and the Midnite Plowboys was sitting in for Craig. There are always anxious moments when something like this happens. Will had not played guitar with us before, and, as a result, we stuck to more standard songs that most of the audience would know.

We had played four or five songs when there was a stir and some commotion in the crowd. Sure enough, out from the curtain behind the Speaker of the House's podium came Roger Kayhart on the arm of Representative Bobby Starr.

Roger was clearly in tough shape and had a hard time moving, but he had a smile on his face. In fact, his smile was radiant as he basked in the spontaneous applause and cheering that greeted him from this full house of admirers and friends.

Roger and Bobby made their way to the front of the Speaker's stand and in front of the band. We had not been clued in as to whether there was to be a ceremony or if there would be remarks by anyone, so the five members of the band just stood in the background to see what would unfold ... when suddenly...

Roger, with no warning, at the top of his lungs, launched into his beloved "You Are My Sunshine." This was the last thing we expected. Instantaneously, Will Lindner looked at me, startled, then instinctively played a G chord to get a reference as to what key Roger might be singing in. Amazingly, even miraculously, Roger was singing in a perfect G. And only a bar or two later, the entire band was accompanying Roger.

Roger's voice was clear and definite and unimpeded by the effects of the serious stroke. He couldn't talk but he could sing, with no negative inflection in his voice. He had begun the song with no reference as to key, and it was a perfect G. Somehow his brain, in that magical moment, had remembered the many many times that Roger had sung "You Are My Sunshine" in the key of G and overcame all of the problems that Roger had experienced during the considerable number of months that he had been incapacitated.

We all played with joy and vigor as Roger sang out verse after verse of that famous song. As he finished with a vocal flourish the House exploded in joy. There wasn't a dry eye in the place. Roger had come home to the House and once again had the legislators in the palm of his hand.

It took a long time for things to settle down after Roger finished. It was one of the more remarkable human events I had ever experienced.

Roger died in 2001 at age 79, having never really recovered from the stroke, but his moment of triumph will be remembered by anyone in that hallowed hall that deep winter evening.

It is only appropriate that a Vermont Legislative Resolution saluting Roger be reprinted here. It captures his colleagues' affection for Roger:

NO. R-66. JOINT RESOLUTION PROCLAIMING ROGER KAYHART TO BE A "REAL VERMONTER." (abridged)

Whereas, Roger Kayhart has made his home in the State of Vermont for nearly a quarter of a century, and

Whereas, Mr. Kayhart was not personally responsible for the fact he was born in Montville, New Jersey, and

Whereas, the only reason Mr. Kayhart claims he didn't relocate to Vermont sooner was because he "didn't hear about Vermont," and

Whereas, Mr. Kayhart is now widely regarded as one of the most honorable residents of the Town of Waltham, Vermont, and

Whereas, he has been a member of that town's Board of Selectmen for 22 years, and

Whereas, the milk from all of his 175 cows is free from the chemical BST, in keeping with Vermont products' reputation for purity and quality, and

Whereas, Roger Kayhart bears the most uncanny digital resemblance to the statue of Ethan Allen which graces the portico of the Vermont State House, and

Whereas, Mr. Kayhart has been a member of the Vermont House of Representatives for the past 11 years, having in his words, "gotten elected by family members," and having served with distinction on the Fish and Wildlife and Agriculture Committees, now therefore be it

Resolved by the Senate and House of Representatives:

That Roger Kayhart be declared by this body to be a "Real Vermonter," and be it further

Resolved: That the Secretary of State be directed to forward two copies of this resolution to Roger Kayhart (the extra copy being for the wall of his milking parlor).

The affection of the Vermont Legislature was very clear.

Thinking of You

I have a brother Joe, who is three years younger than I, who lives in New Jersey. He and his wife are at the stage in their lives where they travel a lot. In that I have also been traveling a lot for my work over the last decade, we will occasionally send greetings to each other from some other place.

I was in my term as Secretary of Vermont's Agency of Human Service in the early 1990s at the time when my brother was traveling and enjoying Italy. He decided to send me a postcard.

The postcard he chose was a close-up of the famous statue of David. This particular postcard focused almost exclusively on David's genitalia. It is quite a picture.

I suppose that he did not know the proper address at the Agency of Human Services offices in Waterbury, so he sent the card addressed to Con Hogan, Secretary of Human Services, State House, Montpelier, Vermont. On the inscription side of the card he wrote cleanly and clearly, "Thinking of you!" and signed it simply, "Joe."

Now, I have no idea what the folks at the State House who received the card thought about what kind of relationship "Joe" and I may have had. As the card made it to and through the State House postal service, I had no idea as to how many people may have seen the card, shown others the card, and otherwise had a good chuckle. But now the card had to be sent to my office through the intrastate mail service, where I'm sure that others also had a chance to see this striking card and the inscription.

Finally, it got to my office in Waterbury. Unbeknownst to me, it was delivered to my secretary, Michelle DellaSanta. Michelle evidently looked at the card and then showed it to quite a few others as she sought advice as to what to do with it.

It is not unusual for the office of the Secretary to receive considerable mail, sometimes of questionable character. We have responsibility in one way or another for the well-being of more than 100,000 Vermonters, some of whom can be very unhappy at one time or another. My secretary would try to protect me from materials that came in the mail that ordinary folks would consider gross or inappropriate. This was one of those moments. Michelle held on to the card.

A day or so later, she mentioned offhand that a postcard had arrived, addressed to me, from "Joe." It appeared to be some kind of crank letter because of the prominence of the genitals on the face of the card, with the inscription, "Thinking of You."

It was at that moment that I realized that it had to have come from my prankster brother. That little postcard had caused quite a stir as it wended its way to my desk. Over the next several days, I received several teasing phone calls from colleagues across State government.

Playing Cards With Dick Snelling

Expectations about politicians can be very high. They are expected to know everything, have a position on everything, and know everyone. Added to that they are expected to make thoughtful solid decisions and be able to execute those decisions perfectly. Such is the life of a Governor of Vermont.

Dick Snelling certainly came close to that expectation. But even the rush of events and information could occasionally get the best of him. One of those moments would be in 1991, when during his inaugural address to the Legislature, he made it clear that our welfare program had to change to become both more cost-effective and to perform better on behalf of the people we were serving.

Over the next few months, my staff and key officials in the Welfare Department, namely Commissioner Veronicas Celani and Deputy Commissioner Jane Kitchel (now a Senator from Caledonia County) worked hard to produce a set of 39 recommendations for changing Vermont's welfare program.

Now came the challenge as to how to gain the full attention of the Governor in the midst of the rush of information he was experiencing. He was in the middle of a recession at the time and, in addition, he had the daily challenges of running the State of Vermont.

Instead of sending the Governor tomes of reports and analyses, I asked Jane and Ronnie to construct a set of "cards" that we would then try to "play" with Governor Snelling. In the words of Sister Elizabeth Candon, Snelling's former Secretary of Human Services, the Governor did not suffer fools gladly, and there was some betting around the office that this gambit just might fall into the fool's category.

But we persisted. We created 39 cards, with each card representing one of the 39 recommendations. On each card was a format that briefly answered several questions. The information might be: the name of the initiative; a description of the initiative; its cost annually and over time;

its benefits over time; who would object to the initiative; who would support it; and several other pertinent statements.

We spiffed the cards up on good stock and made our appointment with the Governor.

When we entered his office, my first utterance was, "Governor, how would you like to play cards with us?" Those who have known Governor Snelling could have predicted the answer, which was along the lines of, "Con, this is serious business. We have large responsibilities, and playing cards is not on my agenda." However, after a little bantering and cajoling we began to play.

One card after another was given to the Governor, and we would quickly discuss its merits. The Governor would then put each card into one of two growing piles, a "no" pile, and a "yes" pile. After an hour most of the cards were in the "yes" pile and we now had an outline for a set of welfare reform initiatives.

It was a difficult few years, which included a special session called by Governor Dean, but the "cards" that were played with Governor Snelling in 1991 stood the test of time under Governor Dean's strong support of the initiatives, and Vermont had its new welfare plan passed by the Legislature and signed by the Governor in 1994. Vermont was the first state in the nation to pass a comprehensive welfare reform plan … all begun with a deck of cards.

The Extraordinary Women of Port Graham, Alaska . . . and their Connection to Vermont

During a working visit I made to Alaska after I had left State government, Alaska's Commissioner of Health and Social Services, Karen Perdue, asked if I would like to accompany her on a visit to an isolated, outlying community, Port Graham. Of course, I jumped at the chance. Susan LaBelle, an Aleut colleague of Karen's, joined us.

Susan was born and raised in Port Graham. Although she had left for the Anchorage region years ago, she still had relatives in the village.

We left a dirt runway in a small Cessna and headed over the Turnagain Fjord through the Kenai Mountains, skirting the Harding Ice Fields. We then aimed for Port Graham, a small Aleut village nestled between the sea and the mountains, several hundred miles away.

From the air, the role fishing had in village life was obvious. A cannery, hatchery, docks, boats, nets, and small dwellings all composed a tranquil picture. We landed on a dirt strip behind the town and worked out a rendezvous time with the pilot, who wanted to head back before loss of light. We agreed to meet at 7:30 P.M. at the airstrip, which gave us almost three hours to visit.

A small sign at the runway welcomed us to Port Graham, a "proud village of Aleut people." The sign indicated a population of 189 people, which was later detailed as 70 families and households with 25 children of elementary school age. We walked about an eighth of a mile down a graveled street, which paralleled the shoreline behind a row of very small, mostly self-made houses. Some were abandoned; others were well kept. All had decades of worn-out machinery or vehicles scattered about, although we later learned that the extent of this disarray had improved greatly over the last few years.

We walked to the community center, a spacious building used for tribal council meetings, community events, and other get-togethers. The building was about 15 years old but was nicely kept up. Rules of the road, admonishments, encouragements, a large U.S. flag, native artwork, and posters covered the walls and gave an inviting impression.

Suddenly, a startling photograph on the wall of an abused young girl with her hands covering her eyes in a pose of shame jolted me back to Vermont. The photograph had been created and used in Vermont about six years ago by Bill Young, the long-standing Commissioner of Social and Rehabilitation Services (SRS) as part of a powerful publication, *Children of a Hidden War,* which was a stark summary of the previous year's child abuse stories and statistics. To see this photo here in a remote Alaskan village clearly told me how small the world is getting and how similar our problems are.

Waiting at the community center to greet us was Elenore McMullen, who was about 60 years old the chief health aide for Port Graham, and also a member of the native village council. Also joining us were Mary Malchoff, an Indian child welfare worker, and Agnes Miller, a village council member and also a health aide. All three were Aleuts.

The next two hours hosted a remarkable conversation.

The women told us that several elders were being abused in the community. Reports to the police, who rarely visit the village, hadn't helped. The visitors prodded the commissioner for her ideas on how to deal with these problems. They seemed satisfied with her concrete suggestions.

At this point, I began to understand that the opportunity to have this conversation was counting more than the actual resolution of the problems.

Also, several older community members were drinking themselves to death, and the tribal council had quietly confronted the offenders. As the conversation about the role of the tribal council unfolded, we began to see the role of the council as fundamental to social control in the village. But this wasn't always so.

The conversation wandered back to 1972, when Elenore came back to the village after many years away. (Children leave the village and go "away" for their secondary education.) After 20 years, Elenore was frightened when she saw the changes upon her return. Elenore told us what life was like in 1972: "Everyone was drinking." It wasn't safe to walk down the little main street. People wandered around openly with bottles in their hands. Child sexual abuse was common, and the odds of a young person escaping abuse were low. In fact, the tribal council itself had been compromised, because some of the members of the council were offenders themselves.

Elenore's story, with constant reinforcement from Susan and the others, became even more compelling. She told of the day when, with great trepidation, she approached the tribal council to tell them she wanted to live in Port Graham again, but she was afraid. Things had to change. The tribal council told her that, if things were going to change, she would have to change them herself. Elenore viewed this as a good thing. The council had not rejected her and, more importantly, the expected backlash had not occurred. She painted us the picture of how, over time, the council began to clean up its own membership and image. One by one, the worst offenders in the town were confronted, and flagrant misbehavior began to subside.

Over the years, needed services were slowly introduced. The most important was the clean, spacious, well-used health clinic, which was built next to the community center only a few years ago. The clinic is staffed with health aides, like Elenore and Mary, who are trained by the Alaskan Health Service. The role of the government in providing health services to Native Americans is essential. These Aleut women told us that the government has served them well. The health clinic is a symbol of progress and hope to the community. Physical fitness classes, weight loss classes, and a variety of other community activities are held here. There is even a "safe" room where a person can "drop out" for a day or two or where someone might sober up without risk of harm. They pointed out plaques on the wall that are reminders of sea rescues, where the clinic played an important role in saving lives.

Later, we took a 5-mile-an-hour car tour of the community. We visited the hatchery, which was brand new, because the other hatchery burned a couple of years ago. Elenore is also the manager of the hatchery. She showed us where they are clearing land and putting in sewer and water lines, so that the villagers can spread out a little, improve their housing, and gain access to these basics. We visited the waste dump, and they showed us how well it is managed. They showed us the woodpiles that are left for people who don't have enough fuel. They showed us the tiny food pan-

try, where they only have to mention to other community members that someone is in need and it fills immediately with donations. They proudly showed us all of the physical improvements in the community that were funded by Exxon Valdez dollars.

The highlight of the conversation came when the women reported that, although serious areas of dysfunction still exist, their community is now safe, developing economically, and has a spirit of accomplishment. The twinkle in Elenore's eye as she told us of the 20-year march toward self-improvement made my day.

The lesson of enlightened leadership in small communities was not lost on me. Vermont has many small rural communities, where almost invisibly, caring community members quietly go about their work caring for their neighbors.

Some things about our communities, no matter where we live, are universal.

I Can't Find Anything That Rhymes With . . .

During the period that I've described as my "period of temporary insanity," as I ran for Governor in 2002, with no party, and an organization of a few amazing people that made it look like I actually had a campaign, there were moments—that I'm sure occur in every campaign—that are to be remembered.

Being a musician and having a bluegrass band that agreed to play occasionally at campaign functions, I naturally had to have a campaign song. That chore fell to Bill Moulton, our mandolin player and a multifaceted musician.

Here, a brief aside is warranted. Bill is a builder of boats, a house builder, and a forestry and wood products expert, to name a few of his many talents. Song writing though, I did not know was in his repertoire.

It wasn't long before the band had a peppy-messaged bluegrass song, which was recorded and played at various functions. It was a good tune that energized people.

One of the people who was advising me at the time was a gentleman by the name of Richard Dresner. Dresner was a first-class professional campaigner who had worked for a wide variety of candidates over the years, including Jim Jeffords. He clearly knew what he was doing and kept me out of the soup on multiple occasions.

He was also working for Governor Mike Huckabee at the time. When he heard the song Bill had done for me, he made it clear that he wanted Bill to write a similar song for the Governor. For Huckabee, a song like this one would be a natural. He was a musician of some accomplishment and had often campaigned playing his electric bass at various functions. And, he had a well-known and well-developed sense of humor. I had earlier known the Governor through my work as President of the American Public Welfare Association (APWA), a national organization. I had found him to be a gregarious and interesting person. When I asked Bill if he would craft the Governor a campaign song, he didn't say much, but he offered to do what he could.

Days and then weeks went by. I had forgotten about my request to Bill as I was wrapped up in the growing activity and intensity of the campaign. But Dick Dresner had not forgotten. He asked me on several occasions about the progress of the song writing. I didn't want to bother Bill, but I finally asked him if he had been able to construct a song for Governor Huckabee.

Bill looked at me ... and in his understated manner ... simply said, "I couldn't find anything that rhymed with Huckabee."

During the last Presidential campaign, I often thought how Governor Huckabee might have done if he had one of Bill Moulton's songs in his bag of tricks.

A Family Affair

In the years when Jeannette and I regularly plied Lake Champlain in our 30-foot Ericson sloop *Bluebird,* we got to know the Lake and its wildlife well.

Our normal routine would be to drive to the lake on Friday afternoon, have a quick visit with Robin Doyle at the International Sailing School on Mallets Bay, pick up the sloop at the mooring, and head out to some remote spot to swim, fish, and generally enjoy the newest Great Lake.

(An aside: In 1998 the Lake became known as the 6th Great lake in the United States. Senator Patrick Leahy used the naming device to make Lake Champlain eligible for federal research and cleanup programs that were designated for the "Great Lakes." Lake Champlain, because it was not a "Great Lake," was not eligible. Senator Leahy, in getting the Lake designated as a "Great Lake" thereby made it eligible for those important resources. There was quick hue and cry of resistance from the politicians of the true and original Great Lakes that was strong enough to negate the Leahy gambit. The final resolution and compromise resulted in Lake Champlain not being designated for "Great Lake" status, but still being eligible for the research and cleanup monies, which was the Senator's objective in the first place.)

One weekend we found ourselves anchored up behind Schuyler Island on the New York side, which lay between Port Kent and Willsboro Bay.

Saturday morning began beautifully with sunshine quickly breaking through the morning fog. We were sitting in the cockpit enjoying the overall peacefulness and a quiet breakfast of milk and Cheerios, when a single female duck came to the transom of the boat. She was apparently begging for a handout. Always ready to oblige, Jan and I each tossed a few Cheerios overboard, which the duck quickly ate. Instead of asking for more, she then headed quickly to shore, maybe 25 yards away.

Less than two minutes later, she reappeared, now being followed by about a dozen very young ducklings in the formation of a perfect V. They swirled around the back of the boat eagerly finishing off a steady stream of Cheerios that we were tossing.

Jan and I quickly figured out that mother duck had come out to see if breakfast was available. When she learned that it was, she tried some of the Cheerios, liked them, and quickly went back to get the entire family, which was also ready for breakfast.

We had witnessed a family affair.

'She Is Doing a Great Job'

We rarely get a chance to tell a story on national-level politicians, simply because we rarely get the chance to work with or be recognized by them. But in 1998 I found myself in that position. In addition to being the Secretary of Human Services for Vermont, I was also President of the American Public Welfare Association (APWA). It was composed of human services administrators from across the country who had the responsibility to implement the new national welfare bill at the state level.

This set of circumstances led to a meeting at the White House. Vice President Al Gore was to preside over the meeting and announce a $1.4 billion boost to the new welfare program. This was also a political event, for it was one of many stages that were set for the Vice President as he prepared to run for President in 2000.

The program was highly scripted. The plan was to have three speakers with brief comments of 10 minutes each, presenting their view of the welfare initiative from their unique perspectives. The three chosen speakers were Silvia Alverez, the Commissioner of the Small Business Administration; Jan Laverty Jones, the Mayor of Las Vegas; and me, representing APWA, in that order. The plan was for the Vice President to be there for each of the three short presentations so he could get a feel for the short talks, and then he was to build on them from his perspective.

Each of the three of us was escorted to the presenters' table along with substantially sized nameplates, and we began our brief remarks. But the Vice President was running late and missed all of the presentations. Just after the three of us were escorted back to the general audience and our nameplates removed from the table, in came the Vice President. He was now going to have to proceed blindly into the program, without the benefit of the content that we had presented.

He started by telling a joke that, frankly, went over flatly. There was little audience response. He then, from notes that had been given to him

by his staff, proceeded to extol each of the three of us for the work we had done in the recent past regarding welfare.

The Commissioner of the SBA was lauded for her work in establishing welfare to work offices throughout the country. The Mayor of Las Vegas was complimented for that city's hiring policy regarding welfare recipients. In my case he went on to say that "Connie Hogan has been a key figure in having Vermont adopt the first statewide welfare program in the country. Not only is she doing a great job in Vermont, but she is also doing a great job at the national level with APWA."

Now the audience by this time knew who I was, as I had just presented to them, and they knew (or I hope they knew) that I wasn't a "she.'"

Of course an audience at the White House is not going to openly laugh at the Vice President of the United States, but there was enough of a light twitter that crossed the room that Mr. Gore knew he had done something wrong, but he didn't know what it was. It was truly an awkward moment for the Vice President.

Then came time for questions and answers with Mr. Gore. After a question or two I worked up my courage and raised my hand and was recognized, at which point I said, "Mr. Vice President, my name is Connie Hogan, and I'm the Secretary of Human Services in Vermont."

The tension was broken, and a good laugh was had by all, including the Vice President.

After all, it's how things end that's important.

The Invisible Man

Deep down I knew we couldn't get away with it. I knew that at some point Commissioner Kent Stoneman and I would bear the wrath of politics for having done something that was unprecedented in governmental arrangements.

The background was . . .

In late 1973 Windsor Prison was on its last legs. The dynamics of closing the prison had reached a dangerous point. The best, least-dangerous inmates had been transferred to the four regional correctional centers in Rutland, South Burlington, St. Johnsbury, and Woodstock. This left the most hard-core, most dangerous prisoners at Windsor as we struggled to beef up the local facilities to handle the tougher prisoners.

At the same time, the best staff, with the most seniority, had also been transferred to the regional facilities, leaving the more inexperienced staff to man the Windsor Prison. This was definitely a recipe for trouble. The leavening effect of the more positive inmates, who wanted no part of trouble, had been lost coincident with their departure to the local facilities. Many of the inmates who were left at the prison were of a frame of the mind that they had nothing to lose by causing trouble, and a culture of defiance and danger was settling into the everyday affairs at old Windsor.

There was also little left of senior and seasoned leadership at the prison. Several of the long-term stalwarts had opted for retirement rather than beginning all over again at the smaller regional facilities, including the long-term warden of the facility, Bob Smith. The leadership vacuum was palpable.

Part of my responsibility as Deputy Commissioner was as project officer for the entire transition. As a result, I was spending most of my time at the Prison. I could see and feel the danger. It felt like every other day there was a close call for one officer or another, and individual inmates, and even groups of inmates, made it their business to make things as miserable as possible for the officer corps that was left.

One day I put in a call to an old friend and colleague in New Jersey, the Director of the New Jersey Department of Corrections. He was Bill Fauver, who was highly regarded in the field as being a straight shooter, both with staff and inmates. I shared my security and safety worries with him and then asked, "Bill, is there anyone in the New Jersey department who is reaching retirement age who is as good as they get on the security and custody front, that you would be willing to assign to Vermont as a security consultant during the next six months? That's the time that it will take to finally close Windsor." Bill thought for a brief moment and said, "I have the perfect man for you . . . Ike Abbott, the Deputy Keeper at Trenton State prison." (Deputy Keeper is the unique name that New Jersey uses to denote head of custody in a correctional facility or prison.)

I knew Ike Abbott from my days in corrections in the New Jersey department. He was a no-nonsense man who demanded orderliness and was known as one of the best, if not the best, custody officer in the State.

To give the reader a sense of how tough Ike really was, I have to tell the following short story: When I was an officer at the Annandale prison in New Jersey, there was a blowup in one of the housing units, and a correction officer was taken hostage. That is serious business. At once, all off-duty officers were called in, and it wasn't long before about 90 officers were standing at parade rest in the middle of the courtyard quadrangle at the prison. It was a hot summer day with the temperature well above 90 degrees. Ike Abbott had recently been borrowed from Trenton prison and had been assigned to Annandale as the temporary head of custody while a permanent head of custody was being recruited.

At this point it is important to describe Ike's physicality. He was six foot four, 220 pounds, and bald as a billiard ball. And there was nothing Ike liked better than a good scrum. He was feared and respected by both the inmates and the officer corps.

Ike had us all lined up in the hot sun. Our expectation was that after a few moments of planning the attack we would rush the housing unit and free our colleague. This event occurred several years prior to the Attica slaughter, and the idea of "never stop talking" had yet to enter the culture of corrections.

For some reason, Ike did not let us go in. He kept us in formation for what seemed to be an hour. And the officers were growing restless as the heat was taking its toll as was the taunting by the inmates from the housing unit.

Finally, out of frustration, an officer in the back of the formation yelled out, "Hey, you bald-headed c---sucker, when are you going to let us go in?" All eyes immediately turned to Ike, who quietly said, with a slight smile on his face, "You are ready," and gave the order to rush the unit. There was so much pent-up energy in the officer corps that it literally took three minutes to break the back of the resistance and to free the officer.

I tell this story, not for the shock value, but to give the reader a sense of the impact of a man like Ike Abbott... and he had now been offered to come to Windsor Prison.

Bill Fauver and I quickly reached a deal. Ike would come to Windsor immediately. We would find an apartment for Ike and his wife, Micky, near the prison. New Jersey would take care of his substantial benefits accrued over the years, and Vermont would pay his salary. And his arrival would be a surprise to the remaining officers and inmates at the prison.

Ike arrived, and without portfolio, immediately took charge of the prison. He spent days and nights there personally supervising the officers and building relationships with the key inmate leadership. He was not without his challenges. One of the boldest escapes by Wayne "Houdini" Carlson (a story told in the previous short-story book) occurred during his watch. But to see this man grab hold of a very difficult and continuing dangerous situation was a sight to behold.

Ike never made the news. The compensation arrangements were all tightly controlled by the department with the quiet help of a few key people in the Salmon administration. On August 14, 1974, Windsor Prison (as Governor Tom Salmon described it … the Old Bastille) closed for good, and Ike quietly made his way back to retirement in New Jersey.

Corrections at its best can be an interesting fraternity. The invisible man was key to one of those moments.

Ross and Gail's Gifts

Ross and Gail Anderson, previously of Shelburne and Charlotte and currently living on Cape Cod are two of the most spiritually generous people I've ever met.

Ross and Gail originally came from Massachusetts, and over the years they have become prominent business people and supporters of improvements in people's lives. Their activities from being members of a religious group that has dedicated itself to the well-being of prisoners, to being supporters of the Committee for the Temporary Shelter for the homeless in Burlington. Ross has also been an active owner of such enterprises as Nordic Ford and the Magic Hat brewery, plus countless other investments and boosts to many small businesses.

One of their gifts to many of their friends is the opportunity to serve as crew on both the old and the new trawlers *10 & 2*. The name symbolizes the idea of 10 years of work, then two years of traveling the seas on their trawler. (Lately many of us have noticed that the ratio has reversed, in that it appears as though they have embarked on a new program of two years of work and 10 years of traveling the seas of the world.)

Three of their gifts to me were the opportunity to travel as crew to remote parts of the world, specifically the west coast of Greenland and Labrador, the Falkland Islands, and, most recently, the coast of Alaska and British Columbia. As a result, over the years I've written short passages and short impressions in my diary that I would like to share in an abridged fashion ... and let the reader be the judge as to their interest. They are presented in honor of Ross and Gail.

In Greenland: August 1997—

"Then we headed toward north Sarqoq and got a lesson in collecting ice for the refrigerator and coolers. We lowered the starboard aft stairs, leaned out with a fish net, and collected enough floating ice pieces to fill the coolers.

"I am at helm again. It is beginning to hit me that we are above the Arctic Circle, and the only people here are Inuit and an occasional Dane." "We are carefully picking our way through an ice field. The weather has cleared. Brilliant blue sky. The icebergs are a bright and brilliant white. Breath taking. Passed an abandoned settlement of Moravian stone houses."

"We are drifting into a bay to have lunch, herring. This narrow passage of a mile or so is very beautiful. I am sitting and enjoying a zero degree C beer, smelling musk ox stew on the stove."

"Paradise found—an unchartered, unmapped, and unsurveyed sound, south of Sarqoq. Great protection, in a deep bowl. We anchored in 25 feet, a quarter mile from the end where two unnamed milky rivers flow from a glacier. The light is spectacular and the mountain has a three-dimensional quality to it."

"Icebergs are sensitive to sound. A deep horn from a boat can result in 'calving.' Icebergs are like clouds, all different, and can be anything you want them to be. I've seen gorillas, ice cream cones, Sing Sing Prison, castles, lions, boats, swans, the Kremlin, all in faithful reproduction. To utter the thought of one of the Danes on board, 'If I were a sculptor, and then saw icebergs, I would give up my craft.'"

"The intelligence of sled dogs, when under harness is extraordinary. The dogs choose the leader. The dogs make decisions about ice conditions and safety. If a dog even threatens a person it is killed immediately. Their canine teeth are filed because of the potential danger."

"One of the things that is very disconcerting is that no one else knows where we are. We are too far from land for VHF, and the Canadians do not cover the northern half of Labrador."

"I still haven't gotten used to using charts where most of the bottom is as yet unsurveyed. It is a good feeling to know that there is still much to be found and learned."

"10:20 P.M.—the Northern Lights. First a whale's tail that covers the entire northern sky. Then the edges of the flukes begin dancing. It is like watching keys move on a pipe organ or watching the pipes themselves move up and down. Large intense balls of light form and then quickly dissipate."

In the Falkland Islands: February 2004—

"On the way into the bay we were accompanied by a pod of dolphins leaping entirely out of the water. It was as if they were glad to see us."

"The water was the color of the Caribbean the closer we got to the brilliant white sand beach. Unfortunately, we could not land because the beach had been mined by the Argentineans (during the Falklands War)."

"As we got closer to the beach we found ourselves in the middle of 20 feeding Jackass penguins. One was actually in the process of regurgitation as we moved through them. The penguins and terns were feeding on something major, and they paid no attention to our presence."

"In the out areas, called 'camp,' there are many stories of odd behavior, such as the friend of Nigel's who traded his fourth wife for a good motorcycle. All stories like this are told with a wink, but with the understanding that there is some modicum of truth to each story.

"As I write this, Gail squeals out, 'There must be 200 sea lions out there.' She's not kidding."

"The penguins are on the next beach. They are the favorite food of the lions. Several times a few of the penguins have tried to get into the water, and each time there were several sea lions waiting. It's an interesting but deadly dance."

"The environment here is barren, stark, forbidding, inhospitable, and any other term you can think of. Why Argentina or anyone else would want it is beyond comprehension. All that said, there is a lonely deep attraction to it. It has to be one of the last places on earth that is so forbidding that people will never overrun it."

"The moon would not rise beyond a spot just over the mountains, nor did it move across the sky. Just stayed in one place. We also had a good look at the southern sky this evening, with Orion, and the Southern Cross, which I had never seen before."

"As the dinghy was making its way to the boat about five small white collison dolphins accompanied it. Suddenly, two of the dolphins took the lead in front of the boat. They were in perfect harmony leading the way. It instantly brought images of some of the classic drawings of the young man in the chariot being drawn by dolphins. Then as if ordered to do so, both of the dolphins split and went their separate ways. It was magnificent. You should have heard all of us hooting and hollering."

"The albatross flies like a precise glider vertical to the waves, flying loops upon loops looking for a morsel."

"We saw a herd of about 20 guanacos, a kind of llama, that were left on the island over 100 years ago."

"Fifteen minutes up the path, I suddenly heard an amazing din of birds from over the next hill, and the dank smell of birds became strong. We came up over the hill together, to suddenly see a sight that we will probably never see again. Overlooking the ocean was a bird rookery, with primarily penguins, all engaged in a din of amazing sound. There were truly thousands of penguins and birds of every color. They were in an amphitheater of rocks and nests surrounding a small harbor from the ocean.

"We all sat down together in disbelief. After a few more steps we were in the middle of this cacophony of sound. Penguins came to greet us. They walked up to us. They looked us in the eye. They brought their friends over. They were so beautifully curious. All I could think about was Ashlyn … and how she would end up embracing them.

"I watched Niels and Ulla sit down about five yards from me. Three penguins in a line approached them. The first one decided to walk between Niels and Ulla. The other two started to follow in line. However, just as the next penguin reached Niels he stopped, put his flipper arm out to stop the penguin behind him ... and they both stood there a minute and thought about passing Niels and Ulla, and finally decided to do it.

"These were all Rock Hopper penguins. They are remarkable in their ability to climb up and down this 200-foot-high rock beach. The rock beach was full of mud-constructed nests for the eggs and babies. Scua flew boldly between the groups of penguins and would try to light and then be in a position to steal eggs. Immediately, penguins from all directions would descend on the scuas. They didn't have a chance.

"We all sat quietly for about an hour, at which point we reluctantly got up and wandered back down this magical path."

"*Penguins and cruise passengers:* Wandering through town with the better part of 1,000 Amsterdam cruise passengers also plying the streets, I was struck by the similarity of these passengers and penguins. The passengers cluster in groups seemingly held together by some kind of centripetal gravity, very similar to penguin clustering. And both species have a similar waddle. They both go to here to there and back again, and both seem to have a vacancy about the eyes. They are both very vulnerable and seem to follow the directions of a few. Finally, cruise ship passengers rarely get to see penguins and penguins don't get to see many passengers."

These are but a few of the "gifts" from Ross and Gail.

Elvis Is on the Other Line

Toward the end of my tenure as Secretary of the Vermont Agency of Human Services, I was invited to a meeting in Morrisville to meet with a group of visiting dignitaries from Europe who were making a study tour of the northeast states and their human service policies and practice. I didn't know much more than that before I arrived at the meeting in the morning. The meeting was being held at the parent–child center in Morrisville, and there was a series of speakers, scheduled to talk briefly, who were primarily from some of the local people services of the area, addressing the dozen or so guests.

I did quickly notice that one of the guests seemed to be somewhat more important than the others. The clues were straightforward. He wore a strongly formal pin-striped suit, was in and out of the room on multiple occasions on his cell phone, and was accompanied by a "PA" or personal assistant. None of the other participants had the amenity of a personal assistant, and certainly none of the Vermont contingency could even envision having such a perquisite.

As the morning meeting came to a close, the pin-striped gentleman had made it known that he would like to visit what was left of our State Hospital, which served the seriously mentally disabled. The hospital had reduced its census steadily over the years to the point where it now stood, at the time, with a small number of patients left, as I recall at about 40 people.

I decided that I would like to be at the meeting at the State Hospital, so I drove back from Morrisville to meet with our pin-striped friend and Rod Copeland, Commissioner of Mental Health at that time.

The three of us were soon in Rod's office, and as we introduced ourselves to each other I learned that the gentleman was Mr. John Hutton, and he was a Deputy Minister of Health for the U.K., a high honor.

Our conversation about mental health policy in Vermont was proceeding nicely, when a call came in for Commissioner Copeland.

At this point I should mention that the workforce of the State Hospital had shrunk to the point where it was necessary for all phone calls coming into the hospital to be routed to the patient living area, where they were accepted by the attendant on duty. If warranted, the call would then be forwarded directly to the Commissioner's office.

After a half hour of conversation, sure enough, a phone call came through for the Commissioner on the speaker phone. It was an attendant in the patient living area who informed the Commissioner that he had just taken a call from a Mr. Tony Blair, who was looking for Mr. John Hutton. The attendant then proceeded to tell Rod Copeland that in a nice way, he had informed Mr. Blair that he couldn't put the call through because "Elvis is on the other line."

John Hutton went white, as he quickly informed Rod and me that Prime Minister Blair was in the process of reorganizing his cabinet of ministers, and that he (Hutton) as Deputy Minister of Health did not know whether he was about to go up or down in the government, and that it *was* Prime Minister Tony Blair calling to let him know which direction it would be.

After a few frantic minutes as Hutton tried to reach the Prime Minister, he finally got through and learned from Blair that, indeed, he was now the Minister of Health for all of the United Kingdom, a very big deal.

It turned out that my wife, Jeannette, and I had arranged a light dinner at our home that evening for the dozen guests from five different countries. You can imagine how often the "Elvis" story was told, each time with more emphasis and hilarity. Our low-key party turned into a great multinational celebration for John Hutton.

After I left the Agency in 1999, I found myself working in England, and I received an invitation to meet with John Hutton at his office near the Parliament. He recounted the Elvis story to a few of his staff in his office, and then offered to give Jan and I a personal tour of Parliament, which resulted in our visiting areas that tourists rarely get a chance to visit, such as the Cromwell Stables, located deep in the innards of the Parliament building.

Another interesting moment during our visit was the view from the floor of the House of Lords. Minister Hutton asked Jan and me to look up to the gallery that surrounds the chamber where visitors and dignitaries could watch the proceedings on the floor. Around the gallery was a brass railing that held a short curtain in place, making the bottom half of the people in the gallery not visible to the Lords. Hutton explained that the curtain was installed in the mid 1960s when ladies skirts had become very short, in the style of the day, with the result that many of the Lords had a hard time concentrating on their work.

It was a heady day for us.

Since then we have watched Mr. Hutton on the BBC's coverage of Parliament as he has continued his service, later as Minister of Transportation and then as Minister of Defense for the U.K.

And this all transpired because of "Elvis" …

What You Never Know Won't Hurt You

Laurie Hulbert is one of the secretaries at the Agency of Human Services. She has been there many years and has served many Secretaries of Human Services extremely well. Laurie and my long-standing personal secretary, Michele DellaSanta, bore the brunt of my quirks as their boss. One of those quirks was to use as much of my drive time around the State to conduct business over the phone. The two women came to dislike the days that I was on the road, because it meant, for them, seemingly endless phone calls. The calls sometimes included extensive dictation, requests to make many phone calls to others, and a variety of assignments that, to them, seemed to go on forever.

From my end of the phone line, this went well. I was able to use my time on the road to work on the multifaceted and complex organization that was the Agency of Human Services.

This system went well for the first six years or so of my tenure, even though there were mild complaints from both Laurie and Michele about how hard it was for them to do business constantly that way. Ordinarily, secretaries use the time that their bosses are away to catch up on their considerable work that accumulates while the boss is in the office. From their point of view I was never giving them a chance to catch up.

At some point in the late 1990s, I began to experience some problems with my phone when on the road. There would begin a kind of crackling sound to the point when Laurie would tell me over the phone, "You are breaking up ... we'll have to talk later."

The problem began to occur ever more frequently. At the same time I was noticing that when I did return to the office that the two women seemed to be in better moods than they had been when the telephone work was in full blast.

Finally, I asked Michele to ask the support group to check out my phone and to make sure that it was in good working order. They checked it and everything looked okay.

At my retirement dinner Michele and Laurie "fessed up."

It turns out that when the two women had had their fill of the work I was constantly giving them over the phone, that Laurie would take a plastic bag, such as a potato chip bag, and begin to crinkle it in front of the receiver. The effect on my end was the crackling noise that led me to believe that phone reception was breaking up. Laurie and Michele became experts at this ruse.

It turns out that I wasn't any less effective in having half the phone time when on the road ... the two secretaries were noticeably happier ... and they were evidently getting great pleasure in knowing that they were outwitting the boss. They enjoyed immensely sharing their techniques with others who had the same phone habits as I did.

Don't let anyone ever try to tell you that bosses are smarter than their secretaries.

'It Got Me to Chelsea and Back'

September 11, 2001, was a terrible day for all of us. It was an additionally difficult day for me. In addition to the carnage in New York, through an almost uncanny set of circumstances it was the day that my daughter, Ruth, and I had to put down two of our closest four-legged friends, our rapidly declining loyal dalmatian, and our first school horse, Morning Cadence, our farm partner's Connemara pony, who over the years had literally taught hundreds of young children how to ride. It really was a terrible day.

In addition, Kathie and Bill Moulton, our long-time farm partners, and my wife, Jeannette, had left on a boat trip, which we kiddingly called our circumnavigation trip. The objective was to leave Alburgh, Vermont, head south on Lake Champlain, through the 14 locks to the Hudson River, then out through the Erie Canal to Lake Ontario, then up to the St. Lawrence to the Richelieu River, and then back into the north end of Lake Champlain.

I was not able to leave Alburgh when they left on the morning of September 10 because of a previously scheduled work commitment. I was chairing a "bipartisan" commission on health care in Vermont, where there was little bipartisanship. The plan was for me to catch up with them by somehow getting to Chipman's Point in Orwell, Vermont, without a car.

My plan was to hire a low-cost local taxi from Barre at the end of the day on the 11th and have the driver take me to Chipman's Point and drop me off. I had made prior arrangement toward this end with Payless Taxi of Barre. Knowing that this could be an expensive taxi ride, I liked the name of the company.

So after a difficult day of watching the horror of the twin towers disaster, and the emotion of putting down and burying two close friends, at the end of the day I called the taxi company and let them know I was ready to leave.

Orwell, Vermont, is a long way from anywhere; from Barre, it's a good 100 miles away. The young man from Payless picked me up at the farm in a sputtering, rattling 1970s vintage Corsair. I threw my duffle bag into the back and off we went. My first inkling that this would be a tough ride was when I asked the young man if he knew where Orwell was. He thought so. The first test for the Corsair was the climb over Lincoln Gap, as the driver chose the cross-country route to Orwell. I just wasn't sure that the old car was going to make it over the Gap, as one of the cylinders had crapped out and our maximum speed over the hill was down to about 12 miles an hour. However, we finally reached the top and coasted down the long western side of the slope.

By now it was about 10:00 P.M. as we slowly made our way across Addison County, with the car now sounding as though it was on its death bed. At one point I asked the young man if he thought it would make it all the way to Chipman's Point, and his response was simply, "Well, last week it got me to Chelsea and back." (Chelsea is 18 miles from Barre.)

By this time there was a steady stream of black smoke coming from the rear-end engine.

Somehow we continued to rattle and smoke our way to the Lake, and at 11:30 P.M. we finally arrived. I paid the young man, and he merrily began the long trip back. I never did hear whether and when he made it back, but at a later time I did calculate the round-trip mileage from Barre to Chelsea (36 miles), and then the round-trip mileage from Barre to

Orwell (200 miles). There is no doubt in my mind that the young fellow had not a clue as to the difference when he took on the job.

Then to cap the day, my next job was to bring Kathie, Bill, and Jeannette up to date on the tragedy in New York. They had been out of communication for the entire day as they made their way south on the Lake ... and had no idea.

Yes, September 11, 2001, was a day to remember.

Tribute to Henry Resolved Mack II

In the spring of 2009, I was reading the morning *Times Argus* and had recently gotten into the light habit of checking the obituaries just to make sure I'm not listed there. At that time I stumbled across the obituary of one Henry Resolved Mack II. My eyes immediately soaked it in.

It was the normal obituary, which indicated the span of Henry's life, and that his grandfather was notable as a past Commissioner of Motor Vehicles in Vermont. For people who didn't know Henry, it would have been hard to determine that Henry was a kind of Renaissance man who reveled in his poetry and his appreciation of nature and his connection to it.

I got to know Henry Resolved Mack II in the 1970s when I was working in the Department of Corrections. I first met him on a visit to the old St. Johnsbury jail on Cherry Street that had been built in the mid 1800s. At first I thought he was a staff member, as he was busy serving meals to the other inmates and generally seemed to be in charge. But he was a "resident" of the facility, making one of his many visits there.

Over the years I developed a delightful relationship with him. Some would call him a vagrant, but he was a man in touch with the natural world. He often lived outdoors and under culverts, was well read, was a poet, and could converse well on just about anything. For several years, when he would spend time in the winter in the warm jails, he would write me poems on toilet paper and send them to me at the Department's central office in Waterbury.

The obituary mentioned that he knew all the policemen in the small towns on a first-name basis.

Here's why.

When it would get cold, Henry would approach a cop and let him know that he was going to steal a candy bar at so and so's store. Sure enough, Henry would enter the store with the police officer in tow behind him, take a candy bar, and be put under arrest, whereby the police

officer would pay for the candy bar and escort Henry to the nearest jail. (His favorite jail was St. Johnsbury, where all of the staff knew and cared for him.) The relationship finally got to the point where the police would escort Henry to St. Johnsbury without even going through the candy bar charade, and the jailers would wink and offer Henry a "room" with no paperwork. Most of the time, Henry's stays at the jail were completely off the book. At the jail he would pitch in with all the chores and the meal service.

On his occasional trips through Waterbury, Henry would stop in and we'd have lunch at the cafeteria, and I would have the chance to catch up on Henry's view of the world.

Given his lifestyle, I never would have believed that Henry would make it to 82 years of age. But he was a man who was at peace with the world, and the world treated him in kind.

There are people like Henry who are around us, but for whom we don't spend much mental energy. We certainly don't extend ourselves for them. I can truly say that Henry enriched my life in gentle ways over the years ... and I hope I helped his.

Madame Speaker

The old adage that each of us is only one, two, or three relationships away from the important people in the world came alive for me in June of 2009.

Dr. Deb Richter, a practicing physician in a Cambridge, Vermont, clinic, and I have been co-authors (along with Dr. Richter's husband, Terry Doran) of several books, articles, and opinion pieces on the increasingly woeful state of affairs of health care in Vermont and the United States. That work, over the last seven years, has brought us into contact with many people from many backgrounds and fields of knowledge. We have visited a wide range of forums including Rotary and Kiwanis clubs, legislative hearings in Vermont, television and radio shows, and book readings. At almost every one of these meetings or moments we have met someone who we didn't expect to meet, resulting in a new friendship, relationship, or insight. Recently, it happened again to us in a rather spectacular manner.

Dr. Richter and I had been invited down to Washington, D.C., to make a presentation to staffers from a variety of committees who had research and drafting responsibilities for the highly controversial health-care bill. The invitation had been extended by Chairman John Conyers of the Judiciary Committee. His staff had read our first book and believed that presentations from us could help Chairman Conyers in his efforts to persuade other representatives that the single-payer approach to reforming health care should not be left off the table of options that were being bandied about at the time.

After an early 6 A.M. flight to Reagan National Airport and attendance at one of the committees taking up the health-care bill, Deb Richter and I made our presentations at a room in the Rayburn Building. The meeting was well attended, and the meeting and presentations went well. John Conyers participated over the entire two-hour length of the meeting. After the meeting was over, he invited us back to his Congressional office.

Conyers, of Michigan, has been in the House of Representatives for more than 30 years, and his office was a renaissance collection spanning all of those years, including an old Kay string bass. The bass struck me as the same vintage as the old Kay bass my wife plays in the Cold Country Bluegrass Band, so Mr. Conyers and I had quite the conversation about the bass.

Then the conversation got down to health care as we reviewed the events of the day and handicapped future possibilities. Conyers was captured by the conversation. He suddenly got up from his chair and grandly announced that it was time for the five of us in the room (Conyers, his Chief of Staff, his Michigan Chief of Staff, Dr. Richter, and me) to pay the Speaker of the House, Nancy Pelosi, a visit.

Imagine the astonished look on my face and Deb Richter's as we got up to make our way down the long hallway from his office to the underground "members only" tram, and then to the Capitol rotunda, where we made our way up several sets of stairways to the rarefied air of Madame Speaker's office.

After making our way past several secretarial guardians, we found ourselves in Mrs. Pelosi's conference room hopefully waiting for a meeting. The first person to come into the room was Wendell Primus, a man whom I had known in the mid-1990s. At that time he was an undersecretary in the Clinton administration and was deeply involved in developing the national welfare reform bill that was adopted by Congress in 1996. I had gotten to know him during that period, as I was President of the national American Public Welfare Association, an arm of the National Governors Association. This organization was active in drafting and weighing in on provisions of the bill. I hadn't seen Wendell since that time (some 13 years prior) and we had quite the unexpected reunion. It turns out that Mr. Primus is Speaker Pelosi's primary health-care advisor.

Wendell then proceeded to tell us that it was unlikely that we would actually meet with the Speaker, but that he would give us a briefing on where the Speaker was standing on health care at this formative time in its debate. Wendell finished his briefing, when, unexpectedly, the door behind him suddenly opened, and in came Speaker Pelosi.

We had a terrific health-care policy discussion for about 20 minutes until the Speaker and Wendell had to leave.

I had been out of government and completely out of touch with the national- and federal-level people I had known, and to be unexpectedly plunged into a small-group conversation with the Speaker of the House of Representatives was, in my mind, a one-in-a-million shot.

As our memorable day continued on the late night flight and the ride back to central Vermont, we mused about the idea that there really are only three degrees of separation among all of us. You never know when and under what circumstances that social law of physics will be expressed.

Afterword

This will likely be my last *Met Along the Way* book. The process of remembering and thinking out loud about all the wonderful people I've met on the journey has been very gratifying to me and, I hope, amusing to the reader. It really is time to end this little series, and there are several good reasons to do so. First, some of the stories are starting to feel a little less relevant in these increasingly gritty times. As I reread them I'm startled about how naïve some of the stories feel about human nature. One example of this sense is how the political process has steadily and slowly descended to a much lower common denominator of character and quality than the colorful leaders of our past. There is a grayness about the discourse that makes it ever more difficult to find the positive gems. (Maybe it's just a product of my growing older. Age tends to give one the advantage and disadvantage of a broad spectrum.)

Secondly, I'm working harder to remember stories of this type. I suppose a total of 75 of these stories is a respectable number of remembrances, but I don't think I could come up with another two dozen or so.

Still, I've been fortunate in having a vocation that allowed me to experience parts of the United States and the rest of the world in order to better understand other people and their joys and sorrows. It also enabled me to meet with and share ideas with some of the "movers and shakers" in America and elsewhere around the globe.

So it is with great pleasure that I thank the readers of the first two books, and those who will read this third book. At the same time, I offer the challenge of remembering and documenting for others your own remembrances and moments that made you pause, perhaps chuckle, and think kindly of the great people that you have "met along the way."